For Stuart —
Sweet dreams always,
enid romarek

# Teddy

*written and illustrated with etchings*
by Enid Warner Romanek

Charles Scribner's Sons • New York

Library of Congress Cataloging in Publication Data
Romanek, Enid Warner.
Teddy.
SUMMARY: Teddy visits the park, takes a nap, paints a
picture, and at the end of the day, retires for the night
with some favorite toys.
[1. Bears—Fiction] I. Title.
PZ7.R6603Te  [E]  78-23177
ISBN 0-684-15811-6

1 3 5 7 9 11 13 15 17 19 RD/C 20 18 16 14 12 10 8 6 4 2

Printed in the United States of America

*For Walter and Barak
and especially for my helper,
Devorah*

Today, like every day, Teddy got up, rubbed his eyes, and went into the bathroom to wash.

Then he dried himself and went downstairs for breakfast.

"Good morning, Mother," said Teddy, giving her a little bear hug.

"Is today the day we're going to the park?"
Teddy asked.
"Yes," said Mother. "Today is the day."

After breakfast Teddy ran back to his room
and dressed.

Mother got out the bicycle. She put Teddy on
his own seat and off they rode.

Mother stopped when they came to the playground in the park, and Teddy hurried over to the sandbox.

He and his friends played hard all morning.

At noon Mother said, "It's time for lunch.
Are you hungry?"
"Yes, yes, yes," said Teddy.

Teddy and Mother walked down the path to the refreshment stand.

Then they sat down and had a picnic.

"Now," said Mother, "it's time to go home."
"No!" said Teddy. "I want to stay and play."
"No," said Mother. "It's time to go."

Back home, Teddy took a nap and had a pleasant dream.

After Teddy woke up, he decided to paint a picture.

Teddy showed the picture to Father when
he came home from work.

At dinner, Teddy told Father all about their day in the park.

"It sounds like a tiring day," said Father.

"I'm not tired," said Teddy.

"I am," said Mother.

Later, Father said, "It's time for bed, Teddy."
"Can't I stay up just a little longer?" asked Teddy.

"No," said Father.
"Bedtime," said Mother.

Slowly, Teddy climbed the stairs.

"Goodnight, Teddy," said Mother with a kiss.

"Goodnight, Teddy," said Father with a big bear hug.

Teddy went into his room.

He took all the little friends he liked to sleep with from the shelf.

Then he rubbed his eyes and went to bed.

*The illustrations for Teddy are from etchings done on
zinc plates printed by the artist on her own etching press.
The lithographic reproductions are printed in duotone.
The text is set in 18 pt. Primer.*

NFL TODAY

THE STORY OF THE

**TAMPA BAY BUCCANEERS**

# THE STORY OF THE TAMPA BAY BUCCANEERS

NATE FRISCH

PUBLISHED BY CREATIVE PAPERBACKS
P.O. BOX 227, MANKATO, MINNESOTA 56002
CREATIVE PAPERBACKS IS AN IMPRINT OF THE CREATIVE COMPANY
WWW.THECREATIVECOMPANY.US

DESIGN AND PRODUCTION BY BLUE DESIGN
ART DIRECTION BY RITA MARSHALL
PRINTED IN THE UNITED STATES OF AMERICA

PHOTOGRAPHS BY ALAMY (JTB PHOTO COMMUNICATIONS), GETTY IMAGES (BRIAN BAHR/ALLSPORT, MARKUS BOESCH/ALLSPORT, SCOTT CUNNINGHAM, JAMES DRAKE/SPORTS ILLUSTRATED, JONATHAN FERREY, FOCUS ON SPORT, GRANT HALVERSON, WESLEY HITT, JED JACOBSOHN, HEINZ KLUETMEIER/SPORTS ILLUSTRATED, ANDY LYONS/ALLSPORT, JIM MCISAAC, J. MERIC, AL MESSERSCHMIDT/NFL, RONALD C. MODRA/SPORTS IMAGERY, MICHAEL MONTES/NFL, PETER MUHLY/AFP, NFL, PETER NOEWCOMB/AFP, LYNN PELHAM/TIME & LIFE PICTURES, TOM PENNINGTON, DOUG PENSINGER, JOE ROBBINS, ELIOT J. SCHECHTER, RICK STEWART/STRINGER, JERRY WACHTER/SPORTS ILLUSTRATED, JEFF ZELEVANSKY)

LIBRARY OF CONGRESS CATALOGING-IN-PUBLICATION DATA
FRISCH, NATE.
THE STORY OF THE TAMPA BAY BUCCANEERS / BY NATE FRISCH.
P. CM. — (NFL TODAY)
INCLUDES INDEX.
SUMMARY: THE HISTORY OF THE NATIONAL FOOTBALL LEAGUE'S TAMPA BAY BUCCANEERS, SURVEYING THE FRANCHISE'S BIGGEST STARS AND MOST MEMORABLE MOMENTS FROM ITS INAUGURAL SEASON IN 1976 TO TODAY.
ISBN 978-1-60818-321-0 (HARDCOVERS)
ISBN 978-0-89812-874-1 (PBK)
1. TAMPA BAY BUCCANEERS (FOOTBALL TEAM)—HISTORY—JUVENILE LITERATURE. I. TITLE.

GV956.T35F75 2013
796.332'640975965—DC23          2012033819

FIRST EDITION
9 8 7 6 5 4 3 2 1

COVER: WIDE RECEIVER VINCENT JACKSON
PAGE 2: RUNNING BACK MIKE ALSTOTT
PAGES 4—5: QUARTERBACK BRAD JOHNSON AND 2004 BUCS OFFENSE
PAGE 6: RUNNING BACK DOUG MARTIN

# TABLE OF CONTENTS

THE BUCS SET SAIL . . . . . . . . . . . . . . . . . . . . . . 8

WHIFFS, LOSSES, . . . AND DUNGY . . . . . . . . . . 18

TAMPA BAY'S TREASURE . . . . . . . . . . . . . . . . . 26

IN SEARCH OF A CAPTAIN . . . . . . . . . . . . . . . 34

## SIDELINE STORIES

REALLY, REALLY BAD . . . . . . . . . . . . . . . . . . . . 13

CELEBRATING THE STREAK'S END . . . . . . . . 17

FASHION STATEMENTS . . . . . . . . . . . . . . . . . . 22

DRAFT DAY DISAPPOINTMENTS . . . . . . . . . . 25

SHIPSHAPE STADIUM . . . . . . . . . . . . . . . . . . . 32

COURTING A COACH . . . . . . . . . . . . . . . . . . . . 41

## MEET THE BUCCANEERS

LEE ROY SELMON . . . . . . . . . . . . . . . . . . . . . . 10

DOUG WILLIAMS . . . . . . . . . . . . . . . . . . . . . . . 16

DERRICK BROOKS . . . . . . . . . . . . . . . . . . . . . . 20

MIKE ALSTOTT . . . . . . . . . . . . . . . . . . . . . . . . . 28

TONY DUNGY . . . . . . . . . . . . . . . . . . . . . . . . . . 38

RONDE BARBER . . . . . . . . . . . . . . . . . . . . . . . . 45

INDEX . . . . . . . . . . . . . . . . . . . . . . . . . . . . . . . 48

TAMPA'S GASPARILLA PIRATE FESTIVAL IS HELD EVERY JANUARY

# The Bucs Set Sail

Long before the city of Tampa, Florida, was officially founded in the mid-1800s, the area was home to American Indian tribes that lived near a bay on the western coast of the Florida Peninsula. In the early 1500s, Spanish explorers seeking gold came upon what is now known as the Tampa Bay area, but finding little treasure, most moved on. It is said, however, that a Spanish pirate captain named José Gaspar was more reluctant to leave, and he returned regularly to the region to raid the ships and camps of other treasure seekers.

Today, the city of Tampa (along with its neighbor, St. Petersburg) still lures in many visitors, but now they come for its resorts, white-sand beaches, and theme parks. Still, residents embrace the region's old swashbuckling history, and Tampa has put a positive spin on the stories of Gaspar by hosting an annual Gasparilla Pirate Festival. The event is so popular that it temporarily doubles the population of Tampa every winter. So it may come as no surprise that when the National Football League (NFL) granted an expansion

END LEE ROY SELMON WAS NAMED DEFENSIVE PLAYER OF THE YEAR IN 1979

# Lee Roy Selmon

**DEFENSIVE END / BUCCANEERS SEASONS: 1976–84 / HEIGHT: 6-FOOT-3 / WEIGHT: 256 POUNDS**

Tampa Bay couldn't afford to waste its first-ever draft choice in 1976. So the new team selected the best player available: Lee Roy Selmon, a huge but humble defensive end from the University of Oklahoma. Selmon earned team Rookie of the Year honors in 1976 and quickly endeared himself to fans and teammates. Although he was known as a genuinely nice guy who helped players up after knocking them down, opponents knew to respect his skills on the field. David Whitehurst, a quarterback with the Green Bay Packers who played against Selmon, called him "the best defensive lineman I've ever seen. He'd make the play, turn around, and line up again. That's how the game is meant to be played." Selmon spent nine years in Tampa and likely would have played longer if a back injury hadn't forced his retirement in 1984. His jersey number, 63, was retired by the Bucs in 1986, and he was inducted into the Pro Football Hall of Fame in 1995. A chain of restaurants in Florida that serves his mother's recipes for chili, meatloaf, and strawberry compote now bears his name.

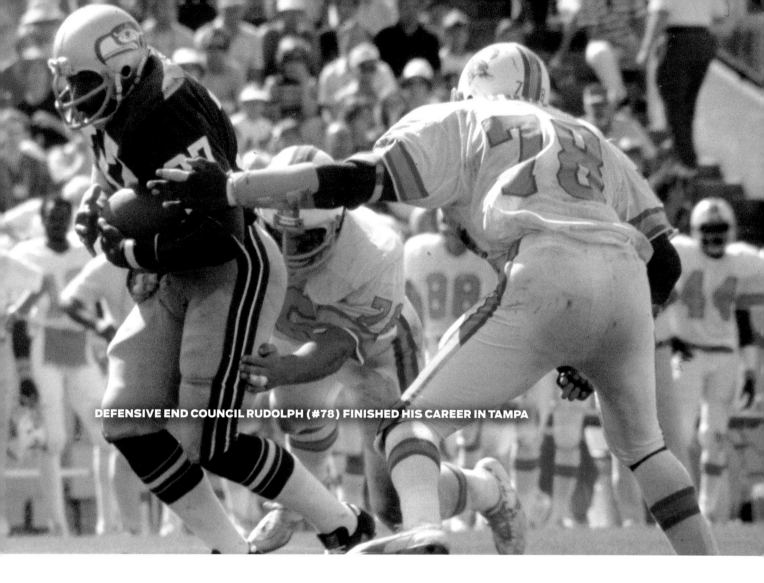

**DEFENSIVE END COUNCIL RUDOLPH (#78) FINISHED HIS CAREER IN TAMPA**

team to the area in the mid-1970s, residents voted to name it the Buccaneers.

Tampa Bay hired John McKay as its first head coach. McKay had previously spent many years successfully coaching at the University of Southern California (USC). The "Bucs" would begin play in 1976, and while fans were eager to see their new team in action, McKay tried to keep expectations realistic. His roster was full of past-their-prime veterans and unpolished rookies, and he said it would take five years for the franchise to round into a contender.

Still, even McKay didn't expect the Buccaneers to be as terrible as they were their first two seasons. In 1976, with veteran quarterback Steve Spurrier leading a disjointed offense, the Bucs couldn't manage to score a point until their third game. They showed a little more cohesiveness as the season went on, yet Tampa Bay lost all 14 of its games that year. "It is at times like this," said McKay, "that we thank our stars that we do have a sense of humor."

But when the losing streak continued deep into the following season, McKay wasn't laughing. Neither was defensive end Lee Roy Selmon, the team's first-round pick in the 1976 NFL Draft. Selmon led a defensive line that included tough ends Council Rudolph and Dave Pear. Tampa Bay's defense was ultimately responsible for introducing the Bucs to the win column on December 11, 1977, when it intercepted six passes and returned an NFL-record three of them for touchdowns. After having lost 26 consecutive games (a more dubious NFL record), the Buccaneers finally notched their first win, 33–14, over the New Orleans Saints.

The Bucs defeated the St. Louis Cardinals at Tampa Stadium the following week and ended the season at 2–12, in last place in the National Football Conference (NFC) Central Division. Still, it was something to build on. And with a new quarterback—the long and lanky Doug Williams, who had been selected in the first round of the 1978 NFL Draft—Tampa Bay seemed poised to climb out of the cellar in its third season. The team had a respectable 4–6 record when Williams's jaw was broken in a game against the Los Angeles Rams. The Bucs won only one more game the rest of the season.

Williams was back in 1979 and better than ever. So was running back Ricky Bell, who rushed for more than 1,000 yards. Tampa Bay won its first five games and eked out a 3–0 victory over the Kansas City Chiefs in the last week of the season to earn both the NFC Central championship and a playoff berth. Just three years after going 0–14, Tampa Bay had achieved a 10–6 record. Jubilant Bucs fans held up banners that read, "From Worst to First."

In the playoffs, Tampa Bay defeated the Philadelphia Eagles 24–17 to reach the NFC Championship Game against the Rams. A victory meant a berth in the Super Bowl. The Buccaneers held their own in a tough defensive battle but came up short, 9–0. "My gosh, we could taste it," said Bucs linebacker Richard Wood. "The Super Bowl. It was right there for us. But you know what? You're not promised anything in this game."

The Buccaneers were not even promised a winning season the following year. In fact, 1980 ended with a disappointing 5–10–1 record, putting Tampa Bay back near the bottom of the standings. But in 1981, with running back James Wilder adding flash to the offense, the Bucs bounced back with a 9–7 record and another division title. This time, however, the Dallas Cowboys drubbed Tampa Bay in the opening round of the playoffs, 38–0.

# Really, Really Bad

The 1976 Tampa Bay Buccaneers weren't just bad. They were really, really bad. They didn't win a single game. Their best running back averaged three yards per carry and scored once all year. Their best receiver caught 30 passes. Tampa's quarterbacks combined to throw 8 touchdowns and 20 interceptions, and they completed less than half their passes. On special teams, the Bucs missed more field goals than they made. As a team, Tampa Bay averaged fewer than 9 points per game while surrendering nearly 30. Their worst loss was a 42–0 thumping at the hands of the Pittsburgh Steelers. In that game, the Buccaneers passed for 57 yards and lost 46 yards on quarterback sacks. Perhaps the best thing about the season was that head coach John McKay was able to put an amusing spin on it. At one point, he said, "Well, we've determined that we can't win at home, and we can't win on the road. What we need is a neutral site." In another instance, he quipped, "Well, we didn't block real good, but we made up for it by not tackling."

**THE CHARISMATIC JOHN McKAY HANDLED DISAPPOINTMENT THROUGH HUMOR**

RICKY BELL'S CAREER PEAKED IN 1979 WITH HIS 1,263 YARDS RUSHING

A players' strike shortened the 1982 season to just 9 games, but the 5–4 Buccaneers were among the 16 teams selected to play in an expanded Super Bowl tournament. As luck would have it, they drew the Cowboys again in the first round and were again defeated, 30–17.

That's when things started unraveling in Tampa Bay. In the off-season, Williams entered into a bitter contract dispute with team owner Hugh Culverhouse that ended the quarterback's tenure with the team. After an embarrassing 2–14 season in 1983 and a career-ending back injury to Selmon in 1984, Coach McKay gave notice as well. His replacement, Leeman Bennett, confidently told fans, "I expect our team to contend for the NFC Central Division title now, not later."

# Doug Williams

QUARTERBACK / BUCCANEERS SEASONS: 1978–82 / HEIGHT: 6-FOOT-4 / WEIGHT: 220 POUNDS

Although he was not the first African American quarterback to play in the NFL, Doug Williams was among the most successful. He was drafted by the Buccaneers with the 17th overall pick in the 1978 NFL Draft and soon made an impact on the hapless team. With Williams under center, the Buccaneers found their way to the playoffs for the first time—and for the second and third times as well. He threw a career-high 20 touchdown passes in 1980 and tallied a total of 73 in his time with the team. Unfortunately, when Williams asked for a raise after leading Tampa Bay to the playoffs in 1982, team ownership countered with a figure that Williams considered unfair. Instead of negotiating, Williams decided to leave the team—angrily. He went on to play two seasons in the rival United States Football League before returning to the NFL and becoming the Most Valuable Player (MVP) of Super Bowl XXII with the Washington Redskins in 1987. After coaching at the college level for several years, Williams returned to Tampa Bay in 2004 as the team's personnel executive.

# Celebrating the Streak's End

The Tampa Bay Buccaneers started celebrating their first win—a 33–14 victory over the New Orleans Saints in December 1977—on the plane ride home to Florida. The players smoked cigars, and coach John McKay made the rounds to shake everyone's hand. But the real celebration began when the plane landed in Tampa and the players found more than 8,000 fans waiting for them at team headquarters, One Buccaneer Place. The streets were too crowded to drive through, so McKay climbed atop a parked car to give a brief speech to the crowd. Fans who had spent 26 games waiting for a win, and who had often chanted "Throw McKay in the Bay" during the losing streak, were now cheering for him. Someone even waved a homemade sign that read, "Retrieve McKay from the Bay!" As the Buccaneer Band played its own version of "When the Saints Go Marching In," changing the refrain to "Oh when the Saints go falling down...," McKay summed up the day's events in one sentence: "It was the greatest victory in the history of the world."

**STEVE SPURRIER WAS NO LONGER WITH THE BUCS WHEN THEY FINALLY STARTED WINNING**

# Whiffs, Losses, ...
# and Dungy

**B**ennett's Bucs had a hard time living up to his expectations. The 1985 season started with nine losses and ended with just two wins. The only bright side was that, as owner of the worst record in the league, Tampa Bay secured the first overall pick in the 1986 NFL Draft. But even that turned disastrous. The team selected Bo Jackson, a fast and powerful running back who had won the Heisman Trophy as college football's best player in 1985. Given the option of signing with the struggling Buccaneers or playing professional baseball, the versatile Jackson chose baseball.

By the end of 1986, the Buccaneers had given up on Bennett, whose two-year record with the team stood at an abysmal 4–28. They had also given up on quarterback Steve Young, who had been sacked 68 times in 2 seasons. Young was traded to the San Francisco 49ers to clear the

QUARTERBACK VINNY TESTAVERDE WAS UNABLE TO RIGHT THE SHIP

# Derrick Brooks

**LINEBACKER / BUCCANEERS SEASONS: 1995–2008 / HEIGHT: 6 FEET / WEIGHT: 235 POUNDS**

By the time he graduated from high school in 1991, Derrick Brooks was already a big-time football star. The young linebacker had led his high school team to a state championship and was regarded as one of the best high school football players in Florida's history. But that was only the beginning. Brooks, a first-round draft pick in 1995, became one of the premier linebackers in the NFL. A prolific tackler who was light enough on his feet to return the occasional interception for a touchdown, Brooks went to the Pro Bowl 10 straight times—becoming 1 of only 4 players in NFL history to do so. But he was respected as much for his efforts off the field as on it. Brooks was well known for his charity work, especially his advocacy for the importance of education. He founded the Brooks' Bunch organization to provide scholarships to youth in the Tampa Bay area and helped start a new high school. In 2003, Florida governor Jeb Bush named him to the Board of Trustees of Florida State University, where Brooks had played college ball.

**BRODERICK THOMAS ON
TAMPA'S LOSING STREAK**

way for young quarterback Vinny Testaverde. Sure that Testaverde was exactly what they needed, the Buccaneers signed him to a 6-year contract worth $8.2 million, making him the richest rookie in the NFL.

New coach Ray Perkins put a lot of faith in Testaverde's arm and in rookie wide receiver Mark Carrier's dependable hands. And to make sure his team would be in great physical shape, Perkins started training camp with three grueling workouts each day. Although that approach appeared to be working when the team routed the Atlanta Falcons 48–10 in the season opener, the players were too tired to keep it up. The Buccaneers finished 4–11 in the strike-shortened 1987 season, then 5–11 in both 1988 and 1989. Before the end of the 1990 season, Perkins was fired.

Tampa Bay's next coach, Richard Williamson, lasted only one season, an embarrassing 3–13 campaign. Former Cincinnati Bengals coach Sam Wyche took the reins in 1992, inheriting a Buccaneers squad that hadn't posted a winning season in 10 years. Unfortunately, even Wyche, who had taken the Bengals to the Super Bowl in 1988, wasn't able to stop that streak in his four seasons with the team.

Part of the team's problem was at the quarterback position. Testaverde had been a disappointment, throwing more interceptions than touchdowns before being released at the end of 1992. But his teammates knew he wasn't the only player to blame. "Everybody wants to say it's Vinny's fault," said linebacker Broderick Thomas. "We've got a young team. He's a young quarterback. He's been taking the rips and hard knocks since he's been here. It ain't his fault."

The closest the Buccaneers came to a winning record under Coach Wyche was a 6–10 season in 1994, when rookie running back Errict Rhett's 192-yard rushing effort against the Washington Redskins was the highlight of a four-game winning streak. But new quarterback Trent Dilfer struggled even more than Testaverde had, throwing 18 interceptions and only 4 touchdown passes in 1995. It was no surprise when Wyche was fired after a 7–9 finish that year. "This team is far better than it was four years ago," Wyche said as he left. "A good man will come in here and reap some of the benefits of the hard work we put in."

# Fashion Statements

It wasn't just the Buccaneers' record that was bad during the early years of Tampa Bay's history. The players wore uniforms that were the epitome of 1970s fashion trends. The combination of bright orange jerseys, white pants, and high orange socks became jokingly known as "creamsicles," after the ice cream treat. The Bucs' white helmets were decorated with red and orange stripes as well as with the image of "Bucco Bruce," an orange pirate wearing a feathered hat and biting on a knife. Remarkably, the Tampa fans proudly wore bold orange outfits to the games. So impressive was the combined effect that when the Philadelphia Eagles came to town for the 1979 playoffs, the Eagles players couldn't help but notice the sea of orange in the stands. "That crowd was the [darndest] thing," laughed Philadelphia linebacker Claude Humphrey. In 1997, the team introduced a new, less-orange look: pewter pants and white jerseys, with orange only outlining dark red numbers. The team unveiled a more swashbuckling logo as well: a skull and two crossed swords on a blood-red pirate flag.

**THE BUCS SUBSTITUTED SWORDS FOR BONES AND ADDED A FOOTBALL TO THEIR LOGO**

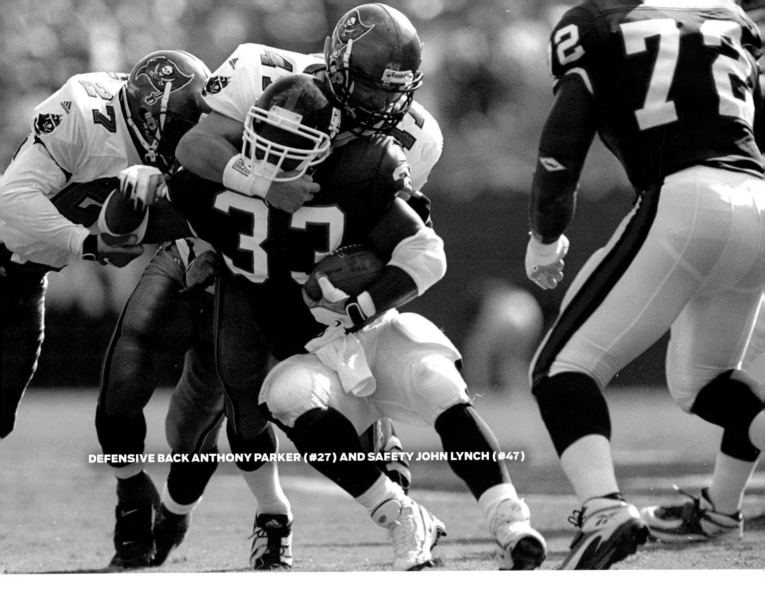

That good man was Tony Dungy, a longtime assistant coach who had earned a reputation as a defensive mastermind with the Minnesota Vikings. When he took over as head coach in 1996, Dungy inherited a trio of young defensive players—tackle Warren Sapp, linebacker Derrick Brooks, and strong safety John Lynch—who would prove pivotal in reversing the team's fortunes. But Dungy was also cursed with a lifeless offense that generated only 20 touchdowns in 16 games in 1996. That season marked Tampa Bay's 14th consecutive losing effort. Neither Dungy nor the young players in white and orange were willing to extend that streak another year.

Something seemed different about the 1997 Buccaneers—and it was more than just the sleek new pewter-and-red uniforms that the players were wearing. After more than a decade of slow starts and sad finishes, Tampa Bay won its first five games. The unlikely hero was former scapegoat Trent Dilfer, whose newfound patience was paying off in the form of more touchdown passes and fewer interceptions.

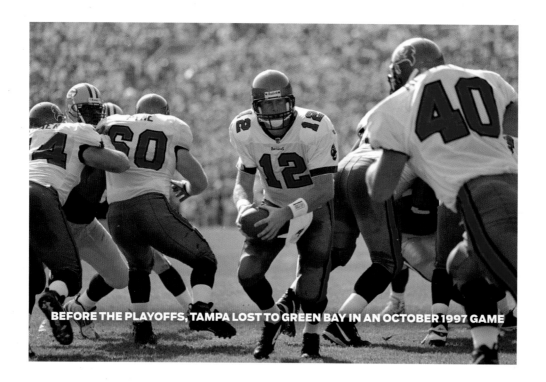

BEFORE THE PLAYOFFS, TAMPA LOST TO GREEN BAY IN AN OCTOBER 1997 GAME

With fullback Mike Alstott bulldozing his way into the end zone and elusive running back Warrick Dunn scampering for nearly 1,000 yards, Tampa Bay's offense was improving.

But it was the defense—led by Sapp, Brooks, Lynch, and linebacker Hardy Nickerson—that stole the show. Tampa Bay's "D" was among the NFL's best in 1997, setting a team record with 44 quarterback sacks. After crushing the Chicago Bears 31–15 in the final game of the regular season, the 10–6 Buccaneers sailed into the postseason. It seemed fitting that the last game ever played in Houlihan's Stadium, as Tampa Stadium had been renamed, was the team's first playoff game in 15 years. And it was a fond farewell, as 73,361 fans showed up to watch the Buccaneers make easy work of the Detroit Lions in the first-round matchup. But then it was on to the frozen tundra of Green Bay's Lambeau Field, where the Super Bowl–bound Packers ended the Buccaneers' season with a 21–7 rout.

# Draft Day Disappointments

The Buccaneers' first-ever draft choice may have been their best: defensive end Lee Roy Selmon, the team's first (and, as of 2013, only) representative in the Pro Football Hall of Fame. Not every selection worked out as well. The Bucs passed over Tony Dorsett, a Hall of Fame running back, in favor of running back Ricky Bell in the 1977 NFL Draft. They used the first overall pick in 1987 on quarterback Vinny Testaverde, who had only a mediocre career in Tampa Bay, while the man he replaced—eventual Hall-of-Famer Steve Young—won three Super Bowl titles with the San Francisco 49ers. The biggest draft debacle, however, may have been using the first overall pick in 1986 to take running back Bo Jackson, even though Jackson had announced that he did not want to sign with the last-place team. Despite a reported 5-year, $7-million contract offer from the Bucs, Jackson opted to play professional baseball with the Kansas City Royals instead. He signed with the Los Angeles Raiders football team in 1987 and played there for four seasons.

**STEVE YOUNG TOOK A LONG TIME TO FIND HIS RHYTHM IN THE PROS**

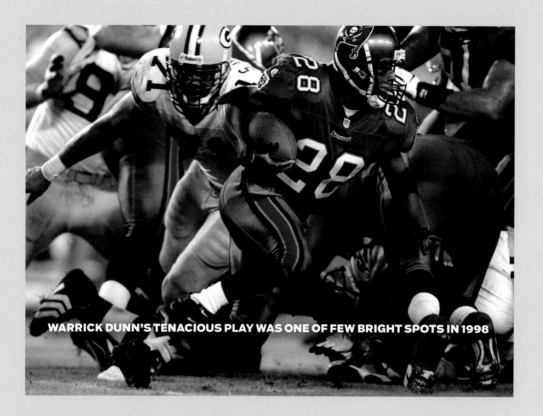

WARRICK DUNN'S TENACIOUS PLAY WAS ONE OF FEW BRIGHT SPOTS IN 1998

# Tampa Bay's Treasure

**T**he Bucs hoped to build on that success when they moved into the brand-new Raymond James Stadium in 1998. And although it won its first game there, the team sputtered through the first half of the season. Even after winning four of its last five games to finish at 8–8, Tampa Bay sat in third place in the NFC Central and out of the playoffs.

The main problem in 1998 was a mediocre offense. Dilfer was just average, with 21 touchdown passes and 15 interceptions, and kicker Michael Husted missed seven key field goals during the season. To add depth at those positions, the Buccaneers selected quarterback Shaun King and kicker Martín Gramática in the 1999 NFL Draft. King took over for Dilfer halfway through the 1999 season and sparked a six-game winning streak, while Gramática kicked 106 total points as a rookie. Despite a 3–4 start, Tampa Bay rebounded to set a franchise record with an 11–5 finish.

The Bucs entered the postseason optimistically. But in the third quarter of the first

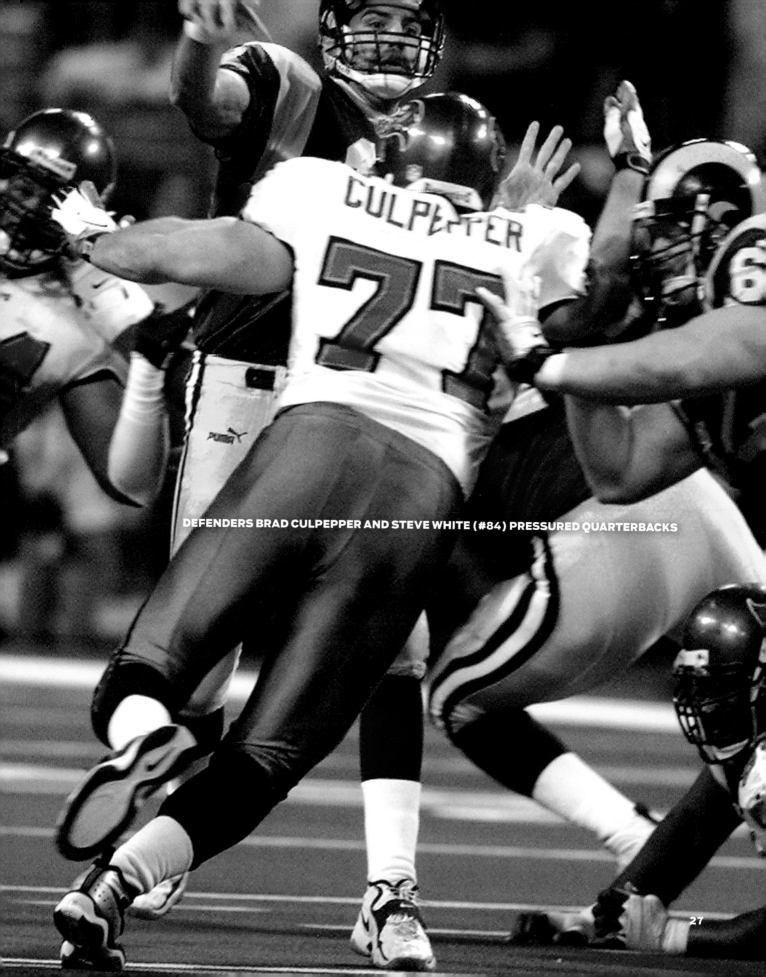

DEFENDERS BRAD CULPEPPER AND STEVE WHITE (#84) PRESSURED QUARTERBACKS

# Mike Alstott

**FULLBACK / BUCCANEERS SEASONS: 1996–2006 / HEIGHT: 6-FOOT-1 / WEIGHT: 248 POUNDS**

There's a reason Mike "The A-Train" Alstott was so good at running over defensive backs and breaking free of tacklers who were trying to bring him down. Part of his training routine during his college career at Purdue University had involved pulling a Jeep through the campus parking lot, then pushing it back. After a workout like that, even the largest defenders weren't much of an obstacle for Alstott. Over the course of his 12 seasons with the Buccaneers, he set a franchise record for touchdowns scored, with 71. Alstott also had the honor of scoring the Bucs' first-ever Super Bowl touchdown on a 15-yard run. For his efforts, Alstott was sent to the Pro Bowl six times and was pictured on the cover of the *NFL Xtreme* video game for PlayStation in 1998. Although Alstott contemplated retirement after both the 2005 and 2006 seasons, it wasn't until a neck injury sidelined him in 2007 that he tearfully announced his retirement from football. "Though mentally I feel like I can continue, physically I can't," he said. "It's been a great ride, an unbelievable ride."

TWO YEARS AFTER BRAD JOHNSON ARRIVED, HE ATTEMPTED A LEAGUE-HIGH 570 PASSES

playoff game against the Redskins, they were down 13–0. Then Lynch made a sensational interception at Tampa Bay's 27-yard line. He ran to the sidelines, where his offensive teammates were standing, spiked the ball, and yelled, "Do something!" Two plays later, Alstott ran the ball into the end zone to make it 13–7. After the Tampa Bay defense recovered a fumble, King tossed a touchdown pass to tight end John Davis, giving Tampa Bay a 14–13 victory.

The following week, the Bucs faced the St. Louis Rams in the NFC Championship Game. Although Tampa Bay's stingy defense limited the normally high-powered Rams to just five points until late in the fourth quarter, St. Louis scored a touchdown with two minutes left to win 11–6. For the second time in franchise history, the Bucs had just missed the Super Bowl.

Coach Dungy knew he had a championship-caliber defense. What he needed was a more productive offense. So, in 2000, the team traded for flamboyant wide receiver Keyshawn Johnson, whose eight touchdown receptions helped lead the Bucs to a 10–6 record and back to the playoffs. In 2001, veteran quarterback Brad Johnson was added to the roster. Unfortunately, both years, the Bucs met

the red-hot Eagles in wintry conditions at Philadelphia's Veterans Stadium in the playoffs. Each time, the Eagles sank the Bucs.

After watching the Buccaneers stumble in the playoffs four times in six seasons, team owner Malcolm Glazer and general manager Rich McKay ran out of patience. And so, two days after the 2001 season ended, McKay fired the immensely popular Dungy. Both fans and players were shocked. "I'm at a loss for words," said cornerback Ronde Barber. "He should be remembered for how he pulled this franchise from the ashes. He made it into something."

Glazer replaced Dungy with former Oakland Raiders coach Jon Gruden. While Dungy had been a low-key teacher known for his defensive expertise, Gruden was a fiery motivator who favored high-powered offenses. Gruden found creative ways

KEYSHAWN JOHNSON SCOOPED UP 106 RECEPTIONS FOR 1,266 YARDS IN 2001

# Shipshape Stadium

For the first two decades of the Tampa Bay Buccaneers' history, the team played at Tampa Stadium, also known as "The Big Sombrero" because its shape resembled the traditional round Mexican hat. The Big Sombrero hosted two Super Bowls and was home to the Buccaneers until 1998, when the team moved to the brand-new Raymond James Stadium. The Buccaneers share the stadium with a local college football team and other annual events, but there's no question who the building was designed for. Just below the upper deck sits a 103-foot-long, 43-ton steel and concrete pirate ship. With an enormous skull mounted on the front and with cannons on the deck that are loaded to launch rubber footballs and confetti when the Bucs score, the ship has become one of the defining images of the team. The lively music played during games adds to the atmosphere: when the song "Yo Ho (A Pirate's Life for Me)" blares out of the public address system, T-shirts, beads, and other prizes are thrown off the ship to the fans below.

**THE CANNONS ONBOARD THE SHIP FIRE ONCE FOR EVERY POINT SCORED**

THE BUCCANEERS' DEFENSIVE LINE PUT UP A UNIFIED FRONT IN 2002

to send his message to players. Before one game, he directed his players' attention to the Raymond James Stadium's replica ship that fired cannons whenever Tampa Bay scored. "See that pirate ship up there? See those guys up there?" he said. "They want to fire the cannons…. So let's put those guys to work…."

In 2002, the cannons did fire frequently as the team scored almost 200 points in 8 home games. But surprisingly, it was the defense that improved the most, giving up fewer points than any team in the league. Relentless defensive end Simeon Rice was among the stars, leading the NFC with 15.5 sacks.

Tampa Bay's franchise-best 12–4 record earned the team a first-round playoff bye before it hosted the 49ers in the second round. The offense and defense came together in a resounding 31–6 victory. The NFC Championship Game would take place once again in Philadelphia's Veterans Stadium. But this time, the tormenting Eagles did not end Tampa Bay's season. The defense did what it had done all year, and in the fourth quarter, Barber picked off a Donovan McNabb pass and ran it back 92 yards for touchdown, sealing a 27–10 victory and the team's first trip to the Super Bowl.

DEXTER JACKSON'S LONGEST INTERCEPTION RETURN (58 YARDS) WAS IN 2002

# In Search of a Captain

Just a year removed from Gruden's coaching stint in Oakland, the Bucs faced the Raiders in Super Bowl XXXVII. The Raiders took an early 3–0 lead, but in a battle of the NFL's pirate teams, Tampa dominated the rest of the way. The Bucs set a Super Bowl record with five interceptions and returned three of them for touchdowns, and Tampa Bay pulled away in a 48–21 blowout. Safety Dexter Jackson, who had snagged two of those interceptions, was named Super Bowl MVP. Although Coach Gruden had been in Tampa only a single season, he was well aware of the hard road Bucs fans had endured, and as he raised the Lombardi Trophy above his head, he shouted, "This night belongs to Tampa Bay!"

Hopes were high for the defending champs going into the next season, but expectations went unmet. Although many players continued to post impressive numbers, as a team, the Bucs didn't dominate the turnover battle the way they had the previous season. Without that critical advantage, Tampa Bay finished with a very average 7–9 record—the club's first losing season since 1996. Lynch and Sapp left the team

THANKS TO BIG HITS BY WARREN SAPP, THE BUCS STEAMROLLED THEIR COMPETITION

RUNNING BACK MICHAEL PITTMAN OWNED THE TEAM RECORD FOR LONGEST TOUCHDOWN RUN

# Tony Dungy

**COACH / BUCCANEERS SEASONS: 1996–2001**

Tony Dungy's name had been mentioned as a candidate for several NFL head coaching positions before he finally landed such a job. A former NFL defensive back who won a Super Bowl with the Pittsburgh Steelers in 1978, Dungy had been an assistant coach for 16 years before being offered the top job in Tampa Bay in 1996. Dungy quickly proved that he was perfect for the position. He introduced his "Cover 2" defensive plan, which relies on speed and agility to be successful, and in his second season with the team, the Buccaneers enjoyed their first winning season in 15 years. Dungy's team made four playoff appearances during his tenure in Tampa, advancing as far as the NFC Championship Game in 1999. Dungy was a soft-spoken man whose Christian upbringing influenced his coaching style; he was known as a patient teacher who tried not to berate or belittle his players. When he couldn't coax enough scoring from his team to reach the Super Bowl, however, he was fired after the 2001 season. In 2006, Dungy won a Super Bowl as coach of the Indianapolis Colts and later became a popular television analyst.

after the season, taking some of Tampa's Bay remaining hope with them. The Bucs played in only one playoff game the next three seasons, plummeting to a 4–12 record in 2006.

Hope reemerged when the Buccaneers brought in journeyman quarterback Jeff Garcia in 2007. Helped by the protection of young tackle Donald Penn, Garcia made the Tampa passing game respectable again and provided the on-field leadership the team had been lacking. "We're going to find a way to clinch this division," Garcia said as the Bucs neared the end of the season with a winning record. "We're going to go into the playoffs, and we're going to battle whoever we have to play."

Tampa Bay did indeed win the division, go to the playoffs, and battle the surging New York Giants. Unfortunately, the Bucs lost 24–14 to the eventual Super

BARRETT RUUD FOLLOWED UP HIS 2008 PERFORMANCE WITH 107 TACKLES IN 2009

Bowl champions. In 2008, versatile linebacker Barrett Ruud helped the Bucs streak to a 9–3 start, but they then lost their last four games. The implosion left Tampa out of the playoffs and Gruden out of a job. The coach was fired and replaced by 32-year-old assistant coach Raheem Morris.

Garcia was also sent packing, and in the 2009 NFL Draft, the Bucs selected towering quarterback Josh Freeman from Kansas State with the 17th overall selection. Freeman began the season on the sidelines, but after Tampa lost six straight games, the youngster was put in and started every game the rest of the season. He led the Buccaneers to only three victories in 2009, but he showed glimpses of brilliance.

In 2010, Freeman emerged as a Tampa Bay star, passing for 3,451 yards and 25 touchdowns. Rookie wide receiver Mike Williams became a favorite target, and another rookie, bruising running back LeGarrette Blount, added ground support to the much-improved passing attack. The young

# Courting a Coach

Jon Gruden wasn't Tampa Bay's first choice. Buccaneers ownership had actually intended to hire longtime NFL coach Bill Parcells to replace Tony Dungy in 2002. When Parcells bowed out, the Bucs appeared ready to snatch coach Steve Mariucci away from the San Francisco 49ers. But then team owner Malcolm Glazer returned from a trip to California with Gruden in tow instead. Even as they were courting Mariucci, the Bucs had also been negotiating with Oakland Raiders owner Al Davis, who expected a lot in return for the young coach who had taken his team to a pair of divisional titles. The two sides finally settled on the terms of what was essentially a trade—Tampa Bay surrendered two first-round draft picks, two second-round draft picks, and $8 million in cash—before Davis called Gruden at 1:00 A.M. to inform him of the decision. By 5:30 A.M., Gruden had agreed to a 5-year, $17.5-million contract to coach the Buccaneers. A year later, at the age of 39, he became the youngest coach ever to win a Super Bowl.

JON GRUDEN WAS LATER CRITICIZED FOR COSTING THE BUCS HIGH DRAFT PICKS

FROM 2004 TO 2009, WIDE RECEIVER MICHAEL CLAYTON AMASSED 221 RECEPTIONS

MARK BARRON KEPT THE HARD HITS COMING IN HIS ROOKIE 2012 SEASON

squad's confidence soared, and after a 4–2 start, Morris publicly made the bold claim, "We're the best team in the NFC."

As the season played out, the Bucs finished with a solid 10–6 record. Unfortunately, 7 NFC teams had at least 10 wins that season, and Tampa Bay was left on the outside looking in when the playoffs began. Still, fans remained optimistic. The baby-faced Bucs had shown great improvement in a single season, and their potential for further improvement looked guaranteed.

Tampa Bay kicked off 2011 with another 4–2 start and appeared on course for the playoffs. Then everything unraveled. Freeman struggled to keep his passes out of enemy hands, and the Buccaneers lost 16 fumbles. While the offense coughed up the ball, the put-upon defense struggled to keep opponents out of the end zone. Tampa gave up an NFL-worst 31 points per game and finished the year by losing 10 straight games.

After the painful collapse, Morris was replaced by Greg Schiano, who had previously turned a lackluster Rutgers University football program into a contender. Tampa then used its first six picks of the 2012 NFL Draft to add young defenders and running backs, including high-energy safety Mark Barron and multipurpose running back Doug Martin. Schiano made it clear he wanted to get the Bucs back to the kind of ball-control offense and aggressive defense that had carried the team to the 2002 Super Bowl.

# Ronde Barber

**CORNERBACK / BUCCANEERS SEASONS: 1997–2012 / HEIGHT: 5-FOOT-10 / WEIGHT: 184 POUNDS**

Throughout Tampa Bay's history, the Buccaneers have featured many defensive standouts, but none was as consistent or versatile as cornerback Ronde Barber. A dangerous defender to throw against, Barber holds the franchise record for interceptions and, on two separate occasions, picked off three passes in a single game. But there was more to Barber than pass coverage, and the small but rugged cornerback annually racked up more tackles than many linebackers. Further enhancing his utility, the cunning defensive back was a threat to blitz the quarterback and tallied nearly 30 sacks in his career. While most corners' effectiveness becomes limited with age, Barber played at a high level into his late 30s and didn't miss a single game for 14 straight years. Perhaps the most memorable day of his career came in the NFC Championship Game in January 2003. In that wintery contest against the Philadelphia Eagles, Barber recorded a sack, forced a fumble, broke up 4 passes, and returned an interception 92 yards for a touchdown. The Bucs clinched the NFC title and went on to win the Super Bowl.

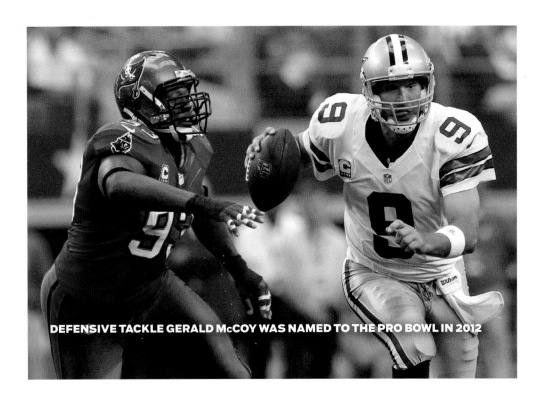

DEFENSIVE TACKLE GERALD McCOY WAS NAMED TO THE PRO BOWL IN 2012

Martin proved to be an astute choice. Installed as the starter before the season began, he ran for a team rookie-record 1,454 yards and added another 472 yards as a receiver. His best game came against Oakland, when he ran for a franchise-record 251 yards and scored 4 times. He was a perfect complement for Freeman, who set new all-time team standards in passing yards (4,065) and touchdown passes (27). The dynamic duo spearheaded overall Tampa Bay all-time bests in total offense (5,820) and points scored (389). The Buccaneers' defense was the stoutest in the NFL against the run, yielding just 82.5 yards a game—still another franchise record. Barron and linebacker LaVonte David contributed significantly to that defense. Yet the Bucs finished just 7–9. That represented a three-game improvement over the previous year, but many Bucs fans thought the season should have been even better. The first seven losses were by eight points or fewer, with two contests being decided by only two points and a third—to the high-flying Atlanta Falcons—slipping past by a single point when a Freeman Hail Mary fell agonizingly short of the end zone.

Like explorers making a long, uncertain journey in hopes of finding riches, the Tampa Bay Buccaneers spent many fruitless years wandering aimlessly before finally claiming the NFL's most coveted treasure—a Super Bowl championship. But now that Tampa Bay's present-day swashbucklers have gotten a taste of football glory, they're eager to continue their assault on the NFL and build up their own legend.

Alstott, Mike 24, 28, 29

Barber, Ronde 30, 33, 45

Barron, Mark 44, 47

Bell, Ricky 12, 25

Bennett, Leeman 15, 18

Blount, LeGarrette 40

Brooks, Derrick 20, 23, 24

Buccaneers name 11

Carrier, Mark 21

Culverhouse, Hugh 15

David, LaVonte 47

Davis, John 29

Dilfer, Trent 21, 23, 26

division championships 12

Dungy, Tony 23, 29, 30, 38, 41

Dunn, Warrick 24

first season 11

Freeman, Josh 40, 44, 47

Garcia, Jeff 39, 40

Glazer, Malcolm 30, 41

Gramática, Martin 26

Gruden, Jon 30, 34, 40, 41

Husted, Michael 26

Jackson, Bo 18, 25

Jackson, Dexter 34

Johnson, Brad 29

Johnson, Keyshawn 29

King, Shaun 26, 29

Lynch, John 23, 24, 29, 34

Martin, Doug 44, 47

McKay, John 11, 13, 15, 17

McKay, Rich 30

Morris, Raheem 40, 44

MVP award 16, 34

NFC Championship Game 12, 29,
    33, 38, 45

NFC championships 45

NFL records 12

Nickerson, Hardy 24

Pear, Dave 12

Penn, Donald 39

Perkins, Ray 21

players' strike 15

playoffs 12, 16, 22, 24, 26, 29, 30,
    33, 38, 39

Pro Bowl 20, 28

Pro Football Hall of Fame 10, 25

Raymond James Stadium 26, 32, 33

retired numbers 10

Rhett, Errict 21

Rice, Simeon 33

Rudolph, Council 12

Ruud, Barrett 40

Sapp, Warren 23, 24, 34

Schiano, Greg 44

Selmon, Lee Roy 10, 11, 15, 25

Spurrier, Steve 11

Super Bowl 28, 33, 34, 41, 44, 45,
    47

Super Bowl records 34

Tampa Stadium 12, 24, 32

team records 24, 26, 28, 33, 45, 47

Testaverde, Vinny 21, 25

Thomas, Broderick 21

uniform change 22, 23

Wilder, James 12

Williams, Doug 12, 15, 16

Williams, Mike 40

Williamson, Richard 21

Wood, Richard 12

Wyche, Sam 21

Young, Steve 18, 25